Along the Way
Documenting My Child's Cancer Journey

Ruth I. Hoffman, MPH

Along the Way: Documenting My Child's Cancer Journey

Author: Ruth I. Hoffman, MPH
Layout Design: Ruth I. Hoffman, MPH

Published by the American Childhood Cancer Organization

Printing History: First Edition September 2010
Second Printing: September 2013

ISBN: 0-9724043-9-2

Disclaimer
The book is written to provide information to assist with the documentation of a child's cancer journey and is not to be used as an alternative to receiving professional advice. Always seek the advice of a trained professional. The American Childhood Cancer Organization has made every effort to ensure that information provided in this resource is accurate at the time of printing, however there is no guarantee that the information will remain current over time. No endorsement of any specific medical procedures, medications, or tests is made herein.

This Book Belongs to: _____

The American Childhood Cancer Organization (formerly Candlelighters Childhood Cancer Foundation) was founded in 1970. It is the largest grassroots organization in the U.S. providing support to children with cancer and their families. Our mission is to provide information and support for children and adolescents with cancer and their families, to provide grassroots leadership through advocacy and awareness, and to support research leading to a cure for all children diagnosed with this life-threatening disease. We are the largest publisher of free childhood cancer books and resources for children with cancer and their families in the U.S.

Hearing that your child or adolescent has been diagnosed with cancer can be overwhelming. As parents of children who have been diagnosed with cancer, we know all too well the importance of keeping track of vital medical information so that it is readily available to communicate as needed with your child's healthcare team. This logbook has been created to help you accomplish that. Its purpose is to assist you with documenting medical treatments, hospital contact information, treatment expenditures as well as a place to add personal notes. Information is also provided about clinical trials, common medical terminologies as well as explanations about common treatment procedures that your child might receive.

I hope that you find this logbook useful and trust that it will help ease some of the burden associated with caring for your child. For additional information including a listing of ACCO's other free resources, or to contact us, visit: www.acco.org or email us at staff@acco.org.

Ruth I Hoffman MPH
Executive Director, ACCO

Outpatient Clinic Weekday Times Open:	Phone:
	Fax:

Outpatient Clinic Evening/Weekend/Holiday:	Phone:
	Fax:

Inpatient Oncology Ward:	Phone:
	Fax:

My Child's Room Number:	Phone:
Date:	

My Child's Room Number:	Phone:
Date:	

My Child's Room Number:	Phone:
Date:	

My Child's Room Number:	Phone:
Date:	

My Child's Room Number:	Phone:
Date:	

My Child's Room Number:	Phone:
Date:	

Notes:

Important Contact Information
Oncology Team Members

Oncologist:	Phone:
	Fax:
	Email:

Nurse Practitioner:	Phone:
	Fax:
	Email:

Head Clinic Nurse:	Phone:
	Fax:
	Email:

Physical Therapist:	Phone:
	Fax:
	Email:

Social Worker:	Phone:
	Fax:
	Email:

Psychologist:	Phone:
	Fax:
	Email:

Child Life Specialist:	Phone:
	Fax:
	Email:

Hospital Pharmacist:	Phone:
	Fax:
	Email:

Your child will also receive care from the Attending Physician (Board certified doctor who specializes in cancer and has supervisory responsibilities; Fellows (Board certified doctor who has completed a pediatric residency and now training in oncology); and Residents (Board certified doctor who is now training in pediatrics).

Family Doc/Pediatrician:	Phone:
	Fax:
	Email:
Community Nurse:	Phone:
	Fax:
	Email:
Community Pharmacist:	Phone:
	Fax:
	Email:
Hospital School Teacher:	Phone:
	Fax:
	Email:
Community Teacher/Tutor:	Phone:
	Fax:
	Email:
Child's School:	Phone:
	Fax:
	Email:
Sibling's School:	Phone:
	Fax:
	Email:
Chaplin:	Phone:
	Fax:
	Email:
Hospice:	Phone:
	Fax:
	Email:

Other:	Phone:
	Fax:
	Email:

Other:	Phone:
	Fax:
	Email:

Other:	Phone:
	Fax:
	Email:

Other:	Phone:
	Fax:
	Email:

Other:	Phone:
	Fax:
	Email:

Other:	Phone:
	Fax:
	Email:

Notes:

*IN CASE OF EMERGENCY CALL 911

Call a member of your oncology team if your child has any of the following symptoms:

- Fever _____ or higher (ask your doctor what temperature). The average normal body temperature is 37 degrees Celsius or 98.6 degrees Fahrenheit.

- Infection: redness, pain or swelling at the central line site, or anywhere on the body. Pain when urinating, and/or having a bowel movement; or pain in other parts of the body.

- Bleeding: Blood in the urine, vomit, or stool (this might look blackish red); nose or gum bleeding that lasts longer than 5 minutes; easy bruising; petechiae (tiny red spots on the skin).

- Chickenpox exposure

- Breathing problems

- Change in alertness, vision or drastic change in personality (conversation doesn't make sense, unable to fully arouse, extremely irritable).

- Diarrhea and/or vomiting accompanied by inability to eat and/or drink.

- Central-line blockage or tear.

- Severe headache when the child wakes up or one that does not go away with Tylenol.

Other:

If after hours and instructed to go to the Emergency Room (ER), be sure to inform the treating physician and/or attending nurse that your child is being treated for cancer.

Have the following information available:

- Child's diagnosis
- Date of last treatment
- Latest blood counts
- Known drug allergies or severe side effects

Be sure that the child does not have their temperature taken rectally. They should also not receive an enema or suppository.

If your child has a fever, it is advised to begin antibiotics as soon as possible.

NOTES:

Clinical Trials

Clinical trials are controlled research studies that test new drugs and other therapies being developed by biotech, pharmaceutical and medical device companies, for both safety and "efficacy." Efficacy means the benefit seen in a clinical study which is used to predict effectiveness in a general population. The ultimate goal of any cancer clinical trial is to evaluate clinical benefit to the patient—specifically a change in either the patient or the tumor that leads to a cure, prolonging of survival, or improvement in symptoms.

Before any cancer therapy is tested in humans, it must be characterized for its chemical ingredients in the laboratory, and then tested in animal studies. Drugs that appear to have activity are tested through animal studies to learn how the drug interacts with a living being as well as to identify side effects that are likely to occur in humans.

Once these initial studies are completed, companies obtain permission from the Food and Drug Administration (FDA) to test in humans. This is done through the filing of an Investigational New Drug (IND) application. A necessary component of the filing is the design and inclusion of a "study protocol." The protocol is a detailed written description of how the clinical study is intended to be done. Clinical studies generally proceed in defined phases.

Notes:

Clinical Trial Phases

Phase I trials involve a small number of patients and are designed to determine the treatment dosage, and preliminary safety information of a drug. Historically, less than 10% of cancer therapies tested in Phase I trials show any positive anticancer results. Phase I trials therefore are not likely to result in a remission or cure. Patients are however given access to new treatments before they are available to others; and the information learned will contribute to medical research to help future patients. There is always the possibility that the patient will receive some benefit.

Phase II trials are larger studies which are more focused on the efficacy of the treatment; e.g. "Does it have activity against a particular disease?" Historically, between a quarter and a third of Phase II trials show some positive results, and in many cases, studies in children may have a higher percentage because therapies are often tested in adults prior to being tested in children.

Phase III studies may follow if a new therapy shows promise during Phase II. Phase III studies are designed to directly compare a new therapy with currently available standard treatment. Direct comparison is the best and most unbiased way to determine which therapy is better. Cancer therapies are most commonly used in combination, so Phase III studies usually compare combinations of drugs where a new drug may be substituted for a currently used one or a new drug may be added to a currently used combination.

Notes:

To assist a patient/patient's family in this understanding, clinical trials must include an 'informed consent' document. The informed consent includes the goals of the trial, a brief explanation about why it is being done, information about the actual treatment, the known risks and benefits of the treatment as well as information about other possible treatments that are currently available (standard care). Contact information for the principle investigators (PI's) of the study are also included in the consent form. Participation in a clinical trial is voluntary. There are no obligations to participate in a trial of an experimental therapy and if a patient does enroll, they are entitled to change their mind and withdraw from the study at any time.

It is important to understand the clinical trial process, as well as available optional treatments for your child before entering into a study. In order to assist families with this decision, additional information can be found at: www.clinicaltrials.gov. For more information about drug development see: www.fda.gov/drugs.

Notes:

Paste
Informed Consent
Here

Diagnosis:
Stage of Disease (if applicable):
Place Where Treated:
Institution Address:
Institution Phone Number:
Date of Diagnosis:
Medical Record Number:
Protocol number (Treatment plan):
Relapse Date (if applicable):
Notes:

A **protocol** is similar to a road map. It's your child's treatment plan. The plan will list the therapy (chemotherapy and other drugs, radiation, surgery, tests), the amounts of therapy, as well as the timeline for when each thing is to happen. This timeline may change depending on how your child responds to therapy. Low blood counts and infections can also cause delays in the treatment timeline.

The protocol can vary in length from 5 pages to 100 pages. There might also be a shortened summary that is 1 to 2 pages in length that you could request. Your child's doctor or nurse practitioner will review the recommended protocol with you. Note that you are legally entitled to receive a copy of your child's full protocol upon request. If your child is entered into a clinical trial, this protocol could be quite extensive as it will include information on which children can be entered into the study, why the scientific study was designed, what the previous studies showed, what the current 'standard of care' is, and what the study is trying to accomplish. If your child is entered into a clinical trial and you want to find out this type of information, you are encouraged to ask your doctor for a copy of the full clinical trial document. Doing so, can make you better informed of the treatment that your child will receive including potential drug reactions, as well as enabling you to keep a watchful eye on dosages given to your child.

Notes:

Paste
Child's Protocol
Summary
Here

Paste
Child's Protocol
Summary
Here

Understanding the procedures that your child will go through will help to reduce fear and anxiety for both you and your child. Prior to any procedure being done, it is good to ask the five 'W's.'

- WHO will be doing the procedure?
- WHAT will be done and WHAT are the side-effects?
- WHEN will it be done?
- WHERE will it be done?
- WHY is it being done?

If your child has extreme difficulty with procedures, ask your medical team if there is a Child Life specialist who can help your child be better prepared.

The following are common procedures that children with cancer experience. Your child's procedures will depend upon the diagnosis and treatment required, so will experience some but not all of the following.

Angiogram: Special x-ray procedure using sedation or general anesthesia to determine the blood supply and circulation in the area surrounding the tumor.

Audiogram: Painless test to measures potential hearing loss. Test is performed in a soundproof room and the results are displayed in the form of a graph and compared with a normal hearing graph.

Auditory Brainstem Response (ABR): Painless test using a 'click' signal delivered through earphones to determine the child's evoked auditory pathway and brainstem function.

Blood draws: Blood taken from the child using either finger poke, the large vein found on the inside of the elbow, or through the child's port. The blood sample is used to determine the CBC (complete blood count), blood chemistries or test for infection.

Biopsy: Surgical removal of cells or tissue from the cancer to determine diagnosis, staging of disease. The tissue can also be used for research purposes.

Blood Transfusion: Process of infusing donated blood/blood products into the child to replenish red blood cells (whole blood transfusions) or platelets (platelet transfusions) that have been depleted as a result of the cancer or the treatment.

Bone Density: Painless x-ray scan of the child's non-dominant hand and wrist with results used to determine age appropriate growth (bone-age).

Bone Marrow Aspirate: Needle removal of semi-liquid bone marrow usually from the back of the hipbone (iliac crest). The resulting cells are used to determine the presence and/or type of cancer (leukemia, lymphoma or presence of CNS disease in brain tumors).

Bone Marrow Biopsy: Surgical removal of small piece of bone to obtain bone marrow.

Bone Scan: Painless nuclear medicine scan using a gamma camera and an IV injection of radioactive material that travels to the bone. Resulting imaging is used to determine the presence of cancer in the bone.

Computed Tomography Scan (CT): Painless x-ray type scan that gives three-dimensional (3D) picture of the child's body. Procedure may take up to one hour so the child might need to be sedated.

Creatinine Clearance: Urine collection in addition to IV blood draw to measure and compare creatinine levels in the blood and urine as a measurement of kidney function.

Echocardiogram (ECHO): Painless sonogram of the heart, using sound waves to create a picture which measures strength and function.

Electrocardiogram/ECG or EKG: Painless measurement of the electrical activity of the heart using electrodes that are placed on the skin of the chest and sometimes legs, with recordings transmitted to a monitor.

Electroencephalogram/EEG: Painless measurement of the electrical activity of the brain using electrodes that are placed on the scalp, with recordings transmitted to a monitor.

Electromyogram (EMG): Test using electrodes to determine the electrical activity of skeletal muscles. Can be done on the surface of the skin or intramuscular (needle and fine wire).

Finger Poke: Small blood drawn from pricking the fingertip with a sharp instrument. Apply Emla cream correctly one hour prior to the procedure to reduce pain.

Gallium Scan (Gallium 67): Type of nuclear medicine imaging requiring venous injection of radioactive gallium citrate 24 to 48 hours prior to the scan.

Gastrostomy: Surgical incision into the stomach and placement of a GI tube to provide direct nutritional support—Total Perenteral Nutrition (TPN).

Glomerular Filtration Rate (GFR): Intravenous injection of a contrast dye to measure the rate of filtration through the kidneys.

Intravenous Pyelogram (IVP): Intravenous injection of a contrast dye visible by x-rays to identify urinary tract abnormalities including the ureters, bladder, and kidneys.

Lumbar Puncture (LP or Spinal Tap): Spinal needle inserted between lumbar vertebrae L3/L4 or L4/L5 for the purpose of collecting cerebrospinal fluid (CNS) for diagnostic purposes, or administration of intrathecal chemotherapy or pain management medication.

Magnetic Resonance Imaging (MRI): Medical scan using magnetic field technology to create two-dimensional image of the brain or spinal cord. Scan may take up to an hour and the machine is loud and tunnel like (may cause claustrophobia) so sedation is often recommended for children.

131 I-meta-iodobenzylguanidine (MIBG): Nuclear medicine imaging technique sometimes used for children with neuroblastoma. Involves IV injection of radioactive material 48 hours prior to the scan, and lengthy scan often requiring sedation to reveal tumor 'hot spots'.

Multi Gated Acquisition Scan (MUGA Scan): Nuclear medicine imaging test used to evaluate the pumping function of the heart ventricles. Procedure requires the child to remain still for approximately 20 minutes so sedation might be given. More accurate than an ECHO, and often used if ECHO shows abnormality.

Neuropsychological Test: Battery of written, performance and oral tests to determine the child's cognitive functioning.

Positron Emission Tomography (PET) Scan: Nuclear medicine imaging technique using minimal radiation dose to the patient.

Treatment Procedures Continued

Pulmonary Function Test: Painless test consisting of blowing air into a tube to determine lung capacity and respiratory functioning.

Venous (External Catheter) Access: Needle injection and/or blood draws into an external catheter previously surgically placed into the right atrium of the heart or the large vein leading to the heart.

Single Photon Emission Tomography (SPECT) Scan: Nuclear medicine imaging test using gamma rays. Multiple two dimensional slices (2D) are combined to provide three-dimensional (3D) information about localized function in internal organs. Similar to PET scans but less expensive.

Subcutaneous Injections: Injections made under the skin. Correctly applying Emla cream or rubbing ice over the site prior to injection can reduce pain and swelling.

Surgery: An operation often used as primary treatment to remove cancerous tissue/tumor and/or take a biopsy specimen to determine a cancer diagnosis.

Temperature Monitoring: Use of a thermometer to detect fever during cancer treatment. Thermometer can be placed under the arm or tongue, or by using a special ear thermometer. Rectal thermometers are not recommended due to possible infection and/or tears leading to infection and bleeding.

Ultrasound Imaging: Portable medical imaging technique using ultrasonography instead of radiation to view muscles, and internal organs.

Urine Sample: Collection of urine either directly into a catch basin (cup, toilet seat hat) or through catheterization if the child is unable to urinate.

Wada Test: Also known as "intracarotid sodium amobarbital procedure (ISAP). Used prior to brain surgery to identify speech and memory centers.

X-Ray: Painless imaging technique using electromagnetic radiation.

Notes:

Blood Counts Explained
Normal Blood Counts

(Reprinted with permission from Childhood Cancer Guides, a charitable nonprofit that publishes helpful books for families of children who have or had cancer—Childhood Leukemia, Childhood Cancer, Childhood Brain & Spinal Cord Tumors, and Childhood Cancer Survivors. www.childhoodcancerguides.org.)

Each laboratory and lab handbook has slightly different reference values for each blood cell, so your lab sheets may differ from the one that appears below. There is also variation in values for children of different ages. For instance, in newborn to 4-year-old children, granulocytes are lower and lymphocytes higher than the numbers listed below. Geographic location affects reference ranges as well. The following table lists blood count values for healthy children:

Blood Count Type	Values for Healthy Children
Hemoglobin (Hgb.)	11.5-13.5 g/100ml.
Hematocrit	34-40%
Red blood count	3.9-5.3 m/cm or 3.9-5.3 x 1012/L
Platelets	160,000-500,000 mm3
White blood count	5,000-10,000 mm3 or 5-10 K/ul
WBC differential:	
• Segmented neutrophils	50-70%
• Band neutrophils	1-3%
• Basophils	0.5-1%
• Eosinophils	1-4%
• Lymphocytes	12-46%
• Monocytes	2-10%
Bilirubin (total)	0.3-1.3 mg/dl
Direct (conjugated)	0.1-0.4 mg/dl
Indirect (unconjugated)	0.2-0.18 mg/dl
AST (SGOT)	0-36 IU/l
ALT (SGPT)	0-48 IU/l
BUN	10-20 mg/dl
Creatinine	0.3-1.1 mg/dl

Notes:

Blood Counts Explained Continued
Complete Blood Count (CBC)

(Reprinted with permission from Childhood Cancer Guides, a charitable nonprofit that publishes helpful books for families of children who have or had cancer—Childhood Leukemia, Childhood Cancer, Childhood Brain & Spinal Cord Tumors, and Childhood Cancer Survivors. www.childhoodcancerguides.org.)

Complete blood counts, or CBCs, are a part of every child's cancer treatment. Blood is taken either from the central line (port) or from a vein and then analyzed and compared to a healthy child's blood counts (see previous chart).

If the values are too far from acceptable ranges, then the treatment schedule may be delayed or changed until your child's counts recover to a more normal range.

Keep in mind that blood counts for your child will vary greatly (both below and above normal values depending on whether it is red blood cell count, white cell count or platelets). The trends in the values will be watched closely by your doctor as they indicate how your child is responding to the treatment, and/or to potential infection.

A decrease in red cell counts could indicate a need for a blood transfusion of packed red cells. Signs and symptoms of low red count (anemia) include fatigue, shortness of breath and pale coloring of the skin.

When platelet levels go down, then a platelet transfusion might be ordered for your child. Symptoms indicating a platelet transfusion might be necessary include easy bruising or small red freckle looking spots on the skin (petechiae) bleeding gums and/or nose bleeding that doesn't stop in 5 minutes or less.

The white blood cell count (WBC) can range from zero to above normal and indicates when a child is able to fight infection.

Notes:

(Reprinted with permission from Childhood Cancer Guides, a charitable nonprofit that publishes helpful books for families of children who have or had cancer—Childhood Leukemia, Childhood Cancer, Childhood Brain & Spinal Cord Tumors, and Childhood Cancer Survivors. www.childhoodcancerguides.org.)

When a child has blood drawn for a complete blood count (CBC), one section of the lab report will state the total white blood cell (WBC) count and a "differential," in which each type of white blood cell is listed as a percentage of the total. For example, if the total WBC count is 1500 mm3, the differential might appear as in the following table:

White Blood Cell Type	Percentage of Total WBCs
Segmented neutrophils (also called polys or segs)	49%
Band neutrophils (also called bands)	1%
Basophils (also called basos)	1%
Eosinophils (also called eos)	1%
Lymphocytes (also called lymphs)	38%
Monocytes (also called monos)	10%

You might also see cells called metamyelocytes, myelocytes, promyelocytes, and myeloblasts listed. These are immature white cells usually only found in the bone marrow. They may be seen in the blood during recovery from low counts.

Notes:

Absolute neutrophil counts (ANC) also called absolute granulocyte count (AGC), are closely watched as they give the physician an idea of your child's ability to fight infection. ANCs vary from zero to in the thousands.

In general, if your child's ANC is **above 1,000** then he/she's **ability to fight infection will be normal.**

To determine the ANC, add the percentages of neutrophils that fight infection (both segmented and band) and multiply by the total WBC. Using the example above, the ANC is 49% + 1% = 50%. 50% of 1,500 (.50 x 1,500) = 750. The ANC in the above example is 750. An **ANC** of **500** to **1000** indicates that your child's ability to **fight infection is depressed** (immunocompromised). An **ANC of less than 500** is called **"neutropenia."** If your child is neutropenic, then he/she should avoid crowds and contact with sources of potential infection.

Notes:

Drugs used to treat cancer often are referred to using different names (Brand Trade name, generic name, other name). The following list will assist you with identifying the chemotherapy drugs being used to treat your child.

Brand Trade Name	Generic Name/Other Name
Accutane	13-cis-retinoic acid/Isotretinoin
Adrucil	5-Fluorouracil/ 5-FU
BiCNU	Carmustine
Blenoxane	Bleomycin
Busulfex/Myleran	Busulfan
Camptosar	Irinotecan/ CPT-11
CeeNU	CCNU/Lomustine
Cerubidine	Daunomycin/Daunorubicin
Cosmegen	Dactinomycin/Actinomycin-D
Cytosar-U	Cytarabine/ARA-C/ Arabinosylcytosine
Cytoxan/Neosar	Cyclophosphamide
DTIC-Dome	Dacarbazine/ DIC
Droxia/Hydrea/Mylocel	Hydroxyurea
Elspar	Asparaginase/L-asparaginase
Etopophos/Toposar	Etoposide/ VP-16
Fludara	Fludarabine
Gleevec	STI-571/Imatinib Mesylate
Hycamtin	Topotecan
Idamycin	Idarubicin
Ifex	Ifosfamide
Leukeran	Chlorambucil
Leustatin	Cladribine/2-CdA
Matulane	Procarbazine
Myleran/Busulfex	Busulfan
Mylotarg	Gemtuzumab Ozogamicin
Oncovin	Vincristine/VCR
Paraplatin	Carboplatin
Platinol	Cisplatin
Temodar	Temozolomide
Thalomid	Thalidomide
Thioplex	Thiotepa/TESPA
Velban	Vinblastine/VLB

Side effects are commonly associated with cancer treatment. The following are a list of known side effects. Some children will experience some, but not all of the following.

Nausea and vomiting
Diarrhea
Fatigue
Low blood counts
Fever
Pain
Weight loss/loss of appetite
Weight gain/increased appetite
Constipation
Dehydration
Mouth and throat sores
Hair loss
Radiation skin burns
Change in smell
Change in taste
Red, itchy, peeling skin, acne
Dry mouth
Somnolence Syndrome (prolonged sleep)
Headaches
Difficulty swallowing
Difficulty speaking
Irritability
Change in blood pressure
Fluid retention
Elevated blood sugar levels
Mood swings
Bed wetting
Pneumonia
Dizziness
Ringing in the ears (tinnitus)
Numbness in fingers and toes
Increased or decreased heart rate
Hemorrhagic cystitis (bleeding from bladder)
Pulmonary edema (fluid retention in lung)
Darkening of the skin
Chills/shaking

Late effects are commonly associated with childhood cancer treatment. The following are a list of known long term effects. Some children will experience some, but not all of the following.

Cataracts
Dry mouth
Hair loss
Cognitive deficits
Tooth decay
Chronic fatigue
Post Traumatic Stress Disorder
Heart Damage
Weak bones
Seizures
Delays in puberty
Venoocclusive disease
Secondary cancer(s)
Thyroid deficiency
Altered growth
Sterility
Depression
Hearing deficit/loss
Amputation
Scoliosis
Renal dysfinction
Chronic hepatitis
Lung damage
Vision problems
Kidney damage
Osteoporosis
Soft tissue damage
Emotional problems
Bone damage
Liver damage
Compromised immune system
Chronic GvHD
Graft vs. Host Disease

Treatment Information: Surgery #1

Date:

Type/Surgical Location:

Name of Surgeon:

Name of Anesthesiologist:

Contact Information:

Complications (if applicable):

Date:
Type/Surgical Location:
Name of Surgeon:
Name of Anesthesiologist:
Contact Information:
Complications (if applicable):

Date:
Type/Surgical Location:
Name of Surgeon:
Name of Anesthesiologist:
Contact Information:
Complications (if applicable):

Treatment Information: Surgery #4

Date:
Type/Surgical Location:
Name of Surgeon:
Name of Anesthesiologist:
Contact Information:
Complications (if applicable):

Date:

Drug Name:	Dose Given:	How Administered (IV, Intrathecal, Oral)

Side Effects/Complications:

Notes:

Date:

Drug Name	Dose Given	How Administered (IV, Intrathecal, Oral)

Side Effects/Complications:

Notes:

Treatment Information
Chemotherapy

Date:

Drug Name	Dose Given	How Administered (IV, Intrathecal, Oral)

Side Effects/Complications:

Notes:

Date:

Drug Name	Dose Given	How Administered (IV, Intrathecal, Oral)

Side Effects/Complications:

Notes:

Date:

Drug Name	Dose Given	How Administered (IV, Intrathecal, Oral)

Side Effects/Complications:

Notes:

Date:

Drug Name	Dose Given	How Administered (IV, Intrathecal, Oral)

Side Effects/Complications:

Notes:

Date:

Drug Name	Dose Given	How Administered (IV, Intrathecal, Oral)

Side Effects/Complications:

Notes:

Date:

Drug Name	Dose Given	How Administered (IV, Intrathecal, Oral)

Side Effects/Complications:

Notes:

Date:

Drug Name	Dose Given	How Administered (IV, Intrathecal, Oral)

Side Effects/Complications:

Notes:

Date:

Drug Name	Dose Given	How Administered (IV, Intrathecal, Oral)

Side Effects/Complications:

Notes:

Date:

Drug Name	Dose Given	How Administered (IV, Intrathecal, Oral)

Side Effects/Complications:

Notes:

Date:

Drug Name	Dose Given	How Administered (IV, Intrathecal, Oral)

Side Effects/Complications:

Notes:

Date:

Drug Name	Dose Given	How Administered (IV, Intrathecal, Oral)

Side Effects/Complications:

Notes:

Date:

Drug Name	Dose Given	How Administered (IV, Intrathecal, Oral)

Side Effects/Complications:

Notes:

Date:

Drug Name	Dose Given	How Administered (IV, Intrathecal, Oral)

Side Effects/Complications:

Notes:

Date:

Drug Name	Dose Given	How Administered (IV, Intrathecal, Oral)

Side Effects/Complications:

Notes:

Chemotherapy

Date:

Drug Name	Dose Given	How Administered (IV, Intrathecal, Oral)

Side Effects/Complications:

Notes:

Date:

Drug Name	Dose Given	How Administered (IV, Intrathecal, Oral)

Side Effects/Complications:

Notes:

45

Treatment Information
Chemotherapy

Date:

Drug Name	Dose Given	How Administered (IV, Intrathecal, Oral)

Side Effects/Complications:

Notes:

Date:

Drug Name	Dose Given	How Administered (IV, Intrathecal, Oral)

Side Effects/Complications:

Notes:

Chemotherapy

Date:

Drug Name	Dose Given	How Administered (IV, Intrathecal, Oral)

Side Effects/Complications:

Notes:

Date:

Drug Name	Dose Given	How Administered (IV, Intrathecal, Oral)

Side Effects/Complications:

Notes:

Treatment Information
Chemotherapy

Date:

Drug Name	Dose Given	How Administered (IV, Intrathecal, Oral)

Side Effects/Complications:

Notes:

Date:

Drug Name	Dose Given	How Administered (IV, Intrathecal, Oral)

Side Effects/Complications:

Notes:

Treatment Information
Chemotherapy

Date:

Drug Name	Dose Given	How Administered (IV, Intrathecal, Oral)

Side Effects/Complications:

Notes:

Date:

Drug Name	Dose Given	How Administered (IV, Intrathecal, Oral)

Side Effects/Complications:

Notes:

Date:

Drug Name	Dose Given:	How Administered (IV, Intrathecal, Oral)

Side Effects/Complications:

Notes:

Date:

Drug Name	Dose Given	How Administered (IV, Intrathecal, Oral)

Side Effects/Complications:

Notes:

Date:
Date:
Date:
Date:
Date:
Area(s) Radiated:
Dose:
Supervising Physician:
Contact Information:
Side Effects/Complications:
Notes:

Treatment Information
Radiation

Date:	
Date:	
Date:	
Date:	
Date:	
Area(s) Radiated:	
Dose:	
Supervising Physician:	
Contact Information:	
Side Effects/Complications:	
Notes:	

Date:
Date:
Date:
Date:
Date:
Area(s) Radiated:
Dose:
Supervising Physician:
Contact Information:
Side Effects/Complications:
Notes:

Date:
Date:
Date:
Date:
Date:
Area(s) Radiated:
Dose:
Supervising Physician:
Contact Information:
Side Effects/Complications:
Notes:

Treatment Information
Radiation

Date:	
Date:	
Date:	
Date:	
Date:	
Area(s) Radiated:	
Dose:	
Supervising Physician:	
Contact Information:	
Side Effects/Complications:	
Notes:	

Treatment Information
Radiation

Date:	
Date:	
Date:	
Date:	
Date:	
Area(s) Radiated:	
Dose:	
Supervising Physician:	
Contact Information:	
Side Effects/Complications:	
Notes:	

Radiation

Date:
Date:
Date:
Date:
Date:
Area(s) Radiated:
Dose:
Supervising Physician:
Contact Information:
Side Effects/Complications:
Notes:

Date and Type of Transplant(s):

Supervising Oncologist:

Contact Information:

Location of Transplant:

Drug Name	Dose Given	How Administered (IV, Intrathecal, Oral)

Side Effects/Complications:

Notes:

Stem Cell Transplant

Date and Type of Transplant(s):

Supervising Oncologist:

Contact Information:

Location of Transplant:

Drug Name:	Dose Given:	How Administered (IV, Intrathecal, Oral)

Side Effects/Complications:

Notes:

Expense Log

Date	Account	Description	Hotel	Transport	Fuel	Meals	Phone	Entertainment	Misc.	TOTAL
										$
										$
										$
										$
										$
										$
										$
										$
										$
										$
										$
										$
										$
										$
			$	$	$	$	$	$	$	

Subtotal $

Total $

Name: _____

Purpose: _____

Reimbursed: _____

To: _____

From: _____

For Period: _____

Notes: _____

AMERICAN
childhood
CANCER ORGANIZATION

Expense Log

Date	Account	Description	Hotel	Transport	Fuel	Meals	Phone	Entertainment	Misc.	TOTAL
										$
										$
										$
										$
										$
										$
										$
										$
										$
										$
										$
										$
										$
										$
		$	$	$	$	$	$	$	Subtotal	$
									Total	$

Name: _____   To: _____

Purpose: _____   From: _____

For Period: _____

Reimbursed: _____   Notes: _____

61

Additional Medication(s) Log

Name _____ Date _____

Name of Medication	Date Started	Date Stopped	Dosage, Dosage Time	Special Instructions	Purpose	Size, Shape, Color	Prescribing Physician	Physician Phone Number	Side Effects	Refill Number	Pharmacy Phone Number

Additional Medication(s) Log

Name _____   Date _____

Name of Medication	Date Started	Date Stopped	Dosage, Dosage Time	Special Instructions	Purpose	Size, Shape, Color	Prescribing Physician	Physician Phone Number	Side Effects	Refill Number	Pharmacy Phone Number

AMERICAN childhood CANCER ORGANIZATION

Temperature Monitoring Log

DATE/TIME	TEMP	DATE/TIME	TEMP	DATE/TIME	TEMP

Temperature Monitoring Log

DATE/TIME	TEMP	DATE/TIME	TEMP	DATE/TIME	TEMP

Date: _____

_____

_____

_____

Date: _____

_____

_____

_____

Date: _____

_____

_____

_____

Date: _____

_____

_____

_____

Date: _____

_____

_____

_____

Date: _____

_____

_____

_____

Date: _____

_____

_____

_____

Date: _____
_____
_____
_____

Date: _____
_____
_____
_____

Date: _____
_____
_____
_____

Date: _____
_____
_____
_____

Date: _____
_____
_____
_____

Date: _____
_____
_____
_____

Date: _____
_____
_____
_____

Date: _____
_____
_____
_____

Date: _____
_____
_____
_____

Date: _____
_____
_____
_____

Date: _____
_____
_____
_____

Date: _____
_____
_____
_____

Date: _____
_____
_____
_____

Date: _____
_____
_____
_____

Date: _____

_____

_____

_____

Date: _____

_____

_____

_____

Date: _____

_____

_____

_____

Date: _____

_____

_____

_____

Date: _____

_____

_____

_____

Date: _____

_____

_____

_____

Date: _____

_____

_____

_____

Date: _____

_____

_____

_____

Date: _____

_____

_____

_____

Date: _____

_____

_____

_____

Date: _____

_____

_____

_____

Date: _____

_____

_____

_____

Date: _____

_____

_____

_____

Date: _____

_____

_____

_____

Date: _____

_____

_____

_____

_____

Date: _____

_____

_____

_____

_____

Date: _____

_____

_____

_____

_____

Date: _____

_____

_____

_____

_____

Date: _____

_____

_____

_____

_____

Date: _____

_____

_____

_____

_____

Date: _____

_____

_____

_____

_____

Journal

Date: _____
_____
_____
_____

Date: _____
_____
_____
_____

Date: _____
_____
_____
_____

Date: _____
_____
_____
_____

Date: _____
_____
_____
_____

Date: _____
_____
_____
_____

Date: _____
_____
_____
_____

Date: _____

_____

_____

_____

Date: _____

_____

_____

_____

Date: _____

_____

_____

_____

Date: _____

_____

_____

_____

Date: _____

_____

_____

_____

Date: _____

_____

_____

_____

Date: _____

_____

_____

_____

Date: _____
_____
_____
_____

Date: _____
_____
_____
_____

Date: _____
_____
_____
_____

Date: _____
_____
_____
_____

Date: _____
_____
_____
_____

Date: _____
_____
_____
_____

Date: _____
_____
_____
_____

74

Date: _____

_____

_____

_____

Date: _____

_____

_____

_____

Date: _____

_____

_____

_____

Date: _____

_____

_____

_____

Date: _____

_____

_____

_____

Date: _____

_____

_____

_____

Date: _____

_____

_____

_____

Date: _____

_____

_____

_____

Date: _____

_____

_____

_____

Date: _____

_____

_____

_____

Date: _____

_____

_____

_____

Date: _____

_____

_____

_____

Date: _____

_____

_____

_____

Date: _____

_____

_____

_____

Date: _____
_____
_____
_____

Date: _____
_____
_____
_____

Date: _____
_____
_____
_____

Date: _____
_____
_____
_____

Date: _____
_____
_____
_____

Date: _____
_____
_____
_____

Date: _____
_____
_____
_____

Date: _____

_____

_____

_____

Date: _____

_____

_____

_____

Date: _____

_____

_____

_____

Date: _____

_____

_____

_____

Date: _____

_____

_____

_____

Date: _____

_____

_____

_____

Date: _____

_____

_____

_____

Date: _____
_____
_____
_____

Date: _____
_____
_____
_____

Date: _____
_____
_____
_____

Date: _____
_____
_____
_____

Date: _____
_____
_____
_____

Date: _____
_____
_____
_____

Date: _____
_____
_____
_____

Date: _____
_____
_____
_____

Date: _____
_____
_____
_____

Date: _____
_____
_____
_____

Date: _____
_____
_____
_____

Date: _____
_____
_____
_____

Date: _____
_____
_____
_____

Date: _____
_____
_____
_____

Date: _____
_____
_____
_____

Date: _____
_____
_____
_____

Date: _____
_____
_____
_____

Date: _____
_____
_____
_____

Date: _____
_____
_____
_____

Date: _____
_____
_____
_____

Date: _____
_____
_____
_____

Date: _____

_____

_____

_____

_____

Date: _____

_____

_____

_____

_____

Date: _____

_____

_____

_____

_____

Date: _____

_____

_____

_____

_____

Date: _____

_____

_____

_____

_____

Date: _____

_____

_____

_____

_____

Date: _____

_____

_____

_____

_____

Date: _____
_____
_____
_____

Date: _____
_____
_____
_____

Date: _____
_____
_____
_____

Date: _____
_____
_____
_____

Date: _____
_____
_____
_____

Date: _____
_____
_____
_____

Date: _____
_____
_____
_____

Journal

Date: _____
_____
_____
_____

Date: _____
_____
_____
_____

Date: _____
_____
_____
_____

Date: _____
_____
_____
_____

Date: _____
_____
_____
_____

Date: _____
_____
_____
_____

Date: _____
_____
_____
_____

Date: _____

_____

_____

_____

Date: _____

_____

_____

_____

Date: _____

_____

_____

_____

Date: _____

_____

_____

_____

Date: _____

_____

_____

_____

Date: _____

_____

_____

_____

Date: _____

_____

_____

_____

Date: _____

_____

_____

_____

Date: _____

_____

_____

_____

Date: _____

_____

_____

_____

Date: _____

_____

_____

_____

Date: _____

_____

_____

_____

Date: _____

_____

_____

_____

Date: _____

_____

_____

_____

Date: _____

_____

_____

_____

Date: _____

_____

_____

_____

Date: _____

_____

_____

_____

Date: _____

_____

_____

_____

Date: _____

_____

_____

_____

Date: _____

_____

_____

_____

Date: _____

_____

_____

_____

Date: _____

_____

_____

_____

Date: _____

_____

_____

_____

Date: _____

_____

_____

_____

Date: _____

_____

_____

_____

Date: _____

_____

_____

_____

Date: _____

_____

_____

_____

Date: _____

_____

_____

_____

Date: _____

_____

_____

_____

Date: _____

_____

_____

_____

Date: _____

_____

_____

_____

Date: _____

_____

_____

_____

Date: _____

_____

_____

_____

Date: _____

_____

_____

_____

Date: _____

_____

_____

_____

Date: _____

_____

_____

_____

Date: _____

_____

_____

_____

Date: _____

_____

_____

_____

Date: _____

_____

_____

_____

Date: _____

_____

_____

_____

Date: _____

_____

_____

_____

Date: _____

_____

_____

_____

Date: _____

_____

_____

_____

Date: _____

_____

_____

_____

Date: _____

_____

_____

_____

Date: _____

_____

_____

_____

Date: _____

_____

_____

_____

Date: _____

_____

_____

_____

Date: _____

_____

_____

_____

Date: _____
_____
_____
_____

Date: _____
_____
_____
_____

Date: _____
_____
_____
_____

Date: _____
_____
_____
_____

Date: _____
_____
_____
_____

Date: _____
_____
_____
_____

Date: _____
_____
_____
_____

Date Treatment Completed:

Recommended Medical Tests:

Organs at Risk:

Recommended Follow-Up Visit Schedule:

Date of First Follow-Up Appointment:

American Childhood Cancer
Organization (ACCO)
10920 Connecticut Ave. Suite A
Kensington, MD 20895
Ph: 855-858-2226; 301-962-3520
Fax: 301-962-3521
http://www.acco.org

American Society for Deaf Children
800 Florida Ave. NE Suite 2047
Washington, DC 20002-3695
800-942-2732 (Voice, TTY)
http://www.deafchildren.org

Amputee Coalition of America (ACA)
9303 Center Street, Suite 100
Manassas, VA 20110
888-267-5669
http://www.amputee-coalition.org

The Association of Cancer Online
Resources Inc. (ACOR)
http://www.acor.org

BMT Infonet
2310 Skokie Valley Road, Suite 104
Highland Park, IL 60035
888-597-7674
http://www.bmtinfonet.org

Cancer Care
275 Seventh Ave. Floor 22
New York, NY 10001
800-813-HOPE (4673)
http://www.cancercare.org

Childhood Cancer Guides
P.O. Box 31937
Bellingham, WA 98228
http://www.childhoodcancerguides.org

Children's Oncology Group
Survivorship Guidelines
http://www.survivorshipguidelines.org

iCANcer App
http://www.itunes.apple.com/us/app/
icancer/id389815324?mt=8

Institute of Medicine
Childhood Cancer Survivorship Report
http://www.iom.edu/
CMS/28312/4931/14782.aspx

Learning Disabilities Association of
America
4156 Library Road
Pittsburgh, PA 15234-1349
412-341-1515
http://www.ldanatl.org

Leukemia & Lymphoma Foundation
1311 Mamaroneck Ave. Suite 310
White Plains, NY 10605
800-955-4572
http://www.lls.org

Make-A-Wish Foundation
4742 N. 24th Street, Suite 400
Phoenix, AZ 85016
800-722-9474
http://www.wish.org

National Cancer Institute (NCI)
5116 Executive Boulevard
Bethesda, MD 20892-8322
800-4-CANCER (422-6237)
http://www.cancer.gov

National Cancer Institute's PDQ
(Physician Data Query)
800-4-CANCER (422-6237)
http://www.cancer.gov/cancertopics/
pdq/cancerdatabase

National Cancer Institute TARGET
(Therapeutically Applicable Research to
Generate Effective Treatments)
http://www.ocg.cancer.gov/programs/
target

National Institute of Health (NIH)
Clinical Trials
http://www.clinicaltrials.gov

Patient Advocate Foundation
421 Butler Farm Road
Hampton, VA 23666
800-532-5274
http://www.patientadvocate.org

Starlight-Starbright Children's
Foundation
2049 Century Park East, Suite 4320
Los Angeles, CA 90067
310-479-1212
http://www.starlight.org

SuperSibs!
660 N. First Bank Drive
Palatine, IL 60067
847-462-4742
http://www.supersibs.org

U.S. Centers for Medicare and Medicaid
Services (CMS)
Health Insurance Marketplace
800-318-2596
http://www.healthcare.gov

U.S. Dept. of Health & Human Services
Children's Health Insurance Program
(CHIP)
http://www.medicaid.gov/CHIP/CHIP-
Program-Information.html

U.S. Dept. of Health & Human Services
Insure Kids Now
877-Kids-Now (543-7669)
http://www.insurekidsnow.gov

U.S. Dept. of Justice
Civil Rights Division
Americans with Disabilities Act
800-514-0301
800-514-0383 (TDD)
http://www.ada.gov